BOTANICAL PRINTS

T&J

Published by TAJ Books International LLC 2013
219 Great Lake Drive,
Cary, North Carolina, USA
27519

www.tajbooks.com

All notations of errors or omissions (author inquiries, permissions)
concerning the content of this book should be addressed to
info@tajbooks.com.

ISBN 978-1-84406-245-4

Printed in China.
1 2 3 4 5 17 16 15 14 13

BOTANICAL PRINTS

T&J

BY SANDRA FORTY

BOTANICAL PRINTS

Flowers by their very nature are fragile and ephemeral, and people have tried to capture and record their transient beauty for as long as the human race has existed. The earliest botanical illustrations are found in ancient herbals—practical works of knowledge, written to pass on crucial information about how to heal the sick. Around the time of the Renaissance, however, flowers began to be more generally appreciated for their beauty, so talented artists set about capturing their magic. Botanical illustration developed into a high art form during the golden era of the 18th and early 19th centuries. From that era, date some of the most stunning examples of botanical art ever made.

Collectors, especially the wealthy men who sent out plant hunters to find new species, commissioned fine botanical artists to portray their latest treasures. It was a matter of pride as well as an appreciation of the art itself.

The earliest plant illustrators used watercolor on vellum (usually calf skin) because vellum's qualities did full justice to the delicate nature of the subject. When the printing press was devised, woodcuts were how plants were shown. The woodcuts were sometimes color tinted by the publisher or the new owner. Then, as printing processes progressed, finer woodcuts were developed, followed by various methods of metal engraving and etching. Occasionally, these were colored but often not. The next advances in printing were various methods of aquaprint, mezzotint, and stippling. Lithography was the next step, and then photography. With the debut of photography, the age of the botanical illustrator was over. This is not to say that the breed has died out; illustrations are still important, but in the face of the digital revolution most botanical works make heavy use of photography.

HERBALS

The very earliest botanical illustrations were intended for descriptive purposes when physicians used plants for medicine and an incorrect plant choice could be fatal. But plants by their very nature are attractive and often highly ornamental, and it was not long before they were being illustrated for their beauty.

The earliest herbals are thought to have been written around 2,000 years ago. They were incredibly valuable sources of reference at a time when healers had few other methods of passing down knowledge to help heal the sick and ailing. These precious books were copied time and again over the centuries—so much so that many illustrations lost their precision and became little more than stylized decoration for the text.

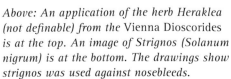

Above: An application of the herb Heraklea (not definable) from the Vienna Dioscorides *is at the top. An image of Strignos (Solanum nigrum) is at the bottom. The drawings show strignos was used against nosebleeds.*

Above: St. Michael's church of Bamberg in Germany dates to the 12th century. The ceiling has paintings of 580 different kinds of plants dating to the 17th century.

5

The earliest known examples of published botanical illustration are found in the five-volume *De Materia Medica* written by the ancient Greek physician and scholar Pedanius Dioscorides. Dioscorides was a traveling physician from Asia Minor who followed the Emperor Nero's army as it campaigned across the Roman Empire. As he journeyed, he talked to the healers, collected the local medicinal herbs, and took notes. He inquired about and discussed their qualities and dangers, learning everything he possibly could from a wide range of sources. Additionally, he made illustrations of the plants he found for greater

and clearer identification purposes.

Dioscorides' work became a monumental reference that was still used 1,500 years later. Its importance was quickly understood and demand arose for copies in all the centers of learning across Europe, India, and the Middle East. Originally written in Greek, it was soon translated into Latin, then Arabic and many other languages, and was eventually supplemented by notes and commentaries from other esteemed physicians from across the known world. It is probable, though, that the very earliest copies were not illustrated.

In the work, Dioscorides lists and discusses the medicinal properties and uses of over a thousand natural medicinal substances, some of them animal and mineral, but the vast majority were plants. Each plant is named, including any local names, then illustrated. He gives a botanical description of the plant along with its habitat, then how to harvest, prepare, and store the plant. Additionally, he lists what properties the plant possesses, how to use it, and what reactions to expect, including bad side effects, as well as how to prepare and administer a suitable dose and any possible ways the substance could be adulterated. Finally, he lists any veterinary uses if applicable.

Dioscorides ordered his work into the therapeutic groupings based on their similar medicinal action—for example, whether a substance is warming, cooling, softening,

Left: European bramble from Dioscorides.

Right: Ulisse Aldrovandi (September 11, 1522–May 4, 1605) was the moving force behind Bologna's botanical garden. This is an illustration in a work on fruit and vegetables.

דודאים Dudaim Hebræis a
לברוחין Iabruchin pluraliter
דודאי Dudai singulariter
ברוח Iabruach Chald.

Μανδραγόρας δλεία
θηλεῖα, βοτάνη

Iabora Serapioni
Lephaa Autrrhoi

Ἀνδροπόνον Dicit' quia hominē interimit
Andritelon ab hominis effigie
Mandragora. Malū caninū Malū terr. Roma
Antimelū Circea. Xeranthes. Antimnien
Antropomorphos-i hiev effigiev Pythagerev
Alæte, Iridacia. Camaron

7

binding, nourishing, relaxing and so on. Every entry was checked and tested, and no plant was included if he had not studied it. The structure of his herbal influenced all following works.

THE ARRIVAL OF PRINTING

In the 16th century, herbals became popular and much more widely available with the advent of the printing press. Many new volumes appeared to provide more invaluable information about the medicinal qualities of plants. Although the pictures were often drawn directly from nature, they were not botanically accurate: little was known even among experts about the science of botany. Usually a short written description of the plant was accompanied by some basic details of the size, flowering season, and color of the plant as well as its medicinal preparation and uses.

With the discovery of the printing press, carved wooden blocks became the norm for creating the illustrations for herbals. Sometimes the illustrations were colored by the publishers—often using a number of colorists which explains the variable quality and colors within a single herbal—while others were colored by the owner when he found the living plant.

During the Renaissance, the style reverted to naturalism in illustration. Even the great Leonardo da Vinci made a few studies and drawings of plants. In the 16th century the study of herbalism was taken very seriously and, for the first time since Dioscorides, scholars studied the plants themselves, rather than relying on rehashed opinions.

Many of the early 16th century herbals were produced in Germany and Switzerland and feature crude woodcuts. This changed in 1530 when the German herbalist Otto Brunfels published his own herbal, the *Herbarum Vivae Eicones* (*Living Plant Images*) with exquisite naturalistic illustrations by Hans Weiditz. This work, published in three parts, is seen as the bridge between classical and medieval works on medicinal plants and the very beginning of modern taxonomy, in particular for the way that life-like woodcuts of the plants were provided for clear identification purposes. Weiditz was a German artist best known for illustrating Petrarch and Cicero, but arguably his finest work was for the herbal. He collected and drew plants from nature and often showed how they changed with the seasons.

LEONHART FUCHS

A few years later, in 1542, the Greek scholar, physician, and university professor Leonhart Fuchs published his herbal, *De Historia Stirpium Commentarii Insignes* (*Notable Commentaries on the History of Plants*). The herbal contained 500 superb woodcuts and around 497 plants described in Latin. Inspired by Brunfels, Fuchs wanted to take the study of plants much further. Each plant was illustrated and described from life. He explained in his introduction that "a picture expresses things more surely and fixes them more deeply in the mind than the bare words of the text." He further remarked, "We have not allowed the craftsmen so to indulge their whims as to cause the drawing not to correspond accurately to the truth."

One of Fuchs's greatest innovations was taking his student physicians on botanical expeditions to study the plants *in situ*. Arranged alphabetically in Greek, *De Historia Stirpium Commentarii Insignes* was quickly published in German, then Latin, French, Spanish, and Dutch. More significantly, it was also published in a smaller pocket edition so that it could be taken on field studies. The woodblocks themselves were reused for 300 years.

PLANT HUNTERS

In the 16th century, Burgundy and Flanders provided the most skilled floral illustrators. Often working from life, their illustrations helped to improve knowledge of the plants themselves. By the 17th century, botanical prints were produced for their beauty alone and were often commissioned by wealthy patrons who wanted a record of the amazing or rare plants in their collection. Plants discovered at the far ends of the world were prestige items, desperately craved and highly prized.

Above: William Withering (1741–1799) wrote the Botanical Arrangement of All the Vegetables Naturally Growing in Great Britain, *the first British book to use the Linaean system.*

9

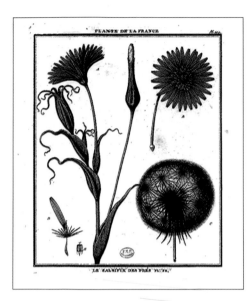

Above: By the 19th century, botanical illustration was extremely sophisticated. This illustration is from Plantes de la France décrites et Peintes d'après nature *(1808).*

The apogee of this, perhaps, could be seen in Holland in February 1637, when tulip bulbs exchanged hands for fabulous amounts. The mania for tulips was short lived and localized to Holland, but the market for beautiful depictions of the bulbs lasted much longer. This was the period in which flower painters were most in demand, especially among the wealthy in France and the Netherlands.

The books of the era featured hand-colored etchings or engravings of botanical illustrations.

With the discovery of many new species, collectors and botanists started to study the specifics of the plants, encouraging the development of scientific botany. Alongside the words were accurate, scientific illustrations. Artistic expression was no longer the prime motive for botanical illustrations; now the science was everything and the illustration was of less importance.

In the 18th century, England became the prime producer of botanical prints, publishing such important works as that of Georg Dionysius Ehret. For a period Ehret worked in close collaboration with the great taxonomist Carl Linnaeus and with George Clifford, a wealthy Dutch banker and keen botanist who was also governor of the Dutch East India Company. In 1738 Clifford funded Linnaeus and Ehret to produce the *Hortus Cliffortianus* containing some thousand plates, half of which were illustrated by Ehret. Ehret next worked for many prestigious institutions including the Royal Society and the Royal Botanic Gardens, Kew. Elsewhere in France, Germany, and Austria, many fine prints were produced as botanical artists could at last have fine reproductions made that fully did justice to their skills.

Roses are many people's favorite flowers and the unchallenged master of painting them was the Flemish artist Pierre Joseph Redouté (1759–1840). Working as an artist, he moved to Paris where—while drawing plants in the Jardin du Roi—he caught the eye of the botanist Charles Louis L'Héritier. Redouté was soon painting exact scientific botanical illustrations for L'Héritier and in time became Marie-Antoinette's official draftsman and Painter to the Queen's Cabinet.

In the late 18th century, making colored prints was a long-drawn-out and painstaking procedure. The engraver would take the artist's painting and carefully engrave a mirror image onto the copper plate using a combination of lines to build up the light and shade. In 1787, Redouté visited London where he learned the technique of stipple engraving which used a combination of dots and lines to create the image, producing a much more delicate and realistic picture. When he returned to Paris, Redouté refined the process and made it his own.

Many of Redouté's illustrations were made into prints. During the 1790s, he was one of the most popular and successful botanical artists. But it is for his pictures of roses that he is best remembered. In 1805, Redouté was appointed court painter to Empress Josephine who employed him to paint the flowers at her garden at Malmaison. Of his many published

Above: Marianne North (1830–1890), a brilliant illustrator, depicted the exotic Nepenthes northiana.

works, *Les Roses*, is the most celebrated. He worked on it between 1817 and 1824. It was published in three volumes and 30 installments over seven years, by which time he had illustrated many of the empress's collection of over 250 rose varieties. By stipple engraving the plates, he mastered a delicacy of technique that made his illustrations more realistic and attractive than those of his contemporaries.

During his lifetime, Redouté painted over 1,800 different plant species and illustrated about 50 botanical books. When he died in 1840, the great age of botanical illustration was over. As the century progressed, enormous scientific progress was made and many new plant species were discovered, but the great flower painters were no longer around to record them.

WILLIAM JACKSON HOOKER

Other notable botanical artists include the great William Jackson Hooker, who became the first director of the Royal Botanic Gardens, Kew, and Regius Professor of Botany at Glasgow University. He also started his own herbarium in Suffolk, England, and in 1826 began an almost 10-year tenure as the chief illustrator of *Curtis's Botanical Magazine.* He signed his work "Hook." Another William Hooker was the official artist of the Royal Horticultural Society in the late 18th and early 19th centuries; his name or initials grace many of the images on the following pages.

In addition to the need for scientifically accurate flower pictures, brightly illustrated picture books of flowers were in demand throughout the 18th and 19th centuries from the educated public. By the second half of the 19th century, cheaply produced periodicals started to appear, but their illustrations were crude and lacked skill. Nevertheless, a market still existed for carefully detailed, botanical books, but most were priced beyond what the ordinary man could afford.

THE ARRIVAL OF PHOTOGRAPHY

With the arrival of photography in the mid-19th century, it was no longer necessary to illustrate plants. Yet botanical artists continued to work, although almost exclusively for botanical institutions and scientific researchers. One of the greatest Victorian artists was Marianne North, an English naturalist and botanical artist (see image on page 11). After the death of her wealthy parents she traveled the further reaches of the world, making intricate paintings of the plants she found. After she exhibited her illustrations in London she offered them—along with a gallery to house them—to the Royal Botanic Gardens, Kew. The offer was accepted and they remain there today on public display. Charles Darwin described to her the wondrous variety of Australian plant life and on his suggestion she journeyed east to both Australia and New

Zealand. By the time she died in 1890 she had worked in the Americas, Japan, and the Far East, India, Australasia, South Africa, and the Seychelles.

CURTIS'S BOTANICAL MAGAZINE

Many of the illustrations in this book come from *Curtis's Botanical Magazine*, which was first published in 1787 when it was called *The Botanical Magazine or Flower-Garden Displayed*. It was started by the London-based apothecary-turned-botanist William Curtis (1746–1799) as an illustrated gardening and botanical journal. The magazine specialized in ornamental and exotic plants, and it was often through its pages that gardeners were introduced to newly discovered plants from around the world. Each plant description was accompanied by highly detailed illustrations. The first illustrations were hand-colored copper engravings; these are now extremely rare and much sought after.

The first 30 volumes used copper engravings for the illustrations and these in turn were colored by as many as 30 people. A typical issue had a print run of 3,000 copies. Curtis himself oversaw 15 volumes before he died. John Sims took over for volumes 15 to 26, at which time the publication became *Curtis's Botanical Magazine*. Mechanical color printing replaced the engravings. At first these were not as beautiful or detailed as the engravings.

The magazine's artists were always carefully trained and always worked closely with the botanists to exactly depict the plant in question. Many great botanical artists worked for the magazine, the first being Sydenham Edwards. The plates were always hand colored until 1948 when a photomechanical process was adopted. In 1826, the eminent botanist William Jackson Hooker took the helm. In time, his son Joseph Hooker replaced him when he became director of Kew Gardens in 1865. The first botanical artist at Kew Gardens was Matilda Smith; between 1878 and 1923, she illustrated over 2,300 plates for the magazine.

For the 10 years between 1984 and 1994, the magazine was called *The Kew Magazine*, but reverted to its historic name in 1995 when it once again became *Curtis's Botanical Magazine*. It is still published quarterly by the Royal Botanic Gardens, Kew, London, and remains a forum for scientific discussion and information for everyone interested in horticultural matters as well as for the merely curious.

AETHUSA CYNAPIUM (Fool's parsley) and
AGARICUS MUSCARIUS (Fly Agaric)
LITHOGRAPH BY AUGUSTUS KÖLLNER, C. 1850

ROSA CANINA

(Dog rose)

Otto Wilhelm Thomé, *Flora von Deutschland, Österreich und der Schweiz*, c. 1885

TOXICODENDRON RADICANS

(POISON IVY)

OTTO WILHELM THOMÉ, *FLORA VON DEUTSCHLAND, ÖSTERREICH UND DER SCHWEIZ*, C. 1885

LYCOPODIUM CATHARTICUM

(NOW *HUPERZIA TETRAGONA*)

ANNALS OF NATURAL HISTORY, 1838

ATELANDRA INCANA AND GASTROLOBIUM CORDATUM

(NOW *HEMIGENIA INCANA AND GASTROLOBIUM SPECTABILE*)

EDWARDS'S BOTANICAL REGISTER, 1839

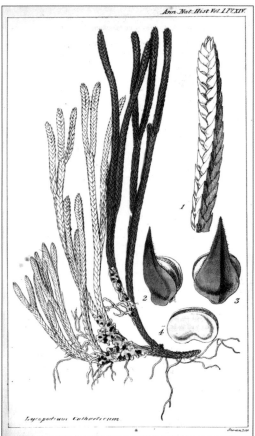

PRIMULA AURICULA

(Mountain cowslip)

Pierre Joseph Redouté, *Choix des Plus Belles Fleurs*, 1827

CAMPSIS RADICANS

(Trumpet vine)

Sydenham Edwards, *The Botanical Magazine*, Vol. 14, 1800

ROSA CENTIFOLIA FOLIACEA

(CABBAGE ROSE)

PIERRE JOSEPH REDOUTÉ, *LES ROSES*, 1824

Rosa Centifolia Bipinnata   *Rosier à feuilles de Celeri*

P.J. Redouté pinx   Imprimerie de Rémond   Langlois sculp

ROSA GALLICA FLORE GIGANTEO

(GALLIC ROSE)

PIERRE JOSEPH REDOUTÉ, *LES ROSES*, 1824

Rosa Gallica flore giganteo.　　*Rosier de Provins à fleur gigantesque.*

PAPAVER ALBUM
(WHITE POPPY)
ULISSE ALDROVANDI, 16TH CENTURY

PAPAVER ROSEUM

(RED POPPY)

ULISSE ALDROVANDI, 16TH CENTURY

CRYSANTHEMI PERUVIANI

(NOW *HELIANTHUS ANNUUS*, SUNFLOWER)
ULISSE ALDROVANDI, 16TH CENTURY

HYACINTHUS

(Double and single hyacinth)

Lithographic & Chromo Company, Rochester, NY, 1879

DOUBLE AND SINGLE HYACINTH.

1. NOBLE PAR MERITE.   2 GRAND LILAC

LILY AND DUNG BEETLE

MARK CATESBY, *NATURAL HISTORY OF CAROLINA, FLORIDA AND THE BAHAMA ISLANDS*, 1731–1743

CANNA GIGANTEA

(Broad-leafed canna)

Pierre Joseph Redouté, *Les Liliacées*, Vol. 6, 1812

AMARYLLIS REGINA VITTATA

BARBARA COTTON, *TRANSACTIONS OF THE HORTICULTURAL SOCIETY OF LONDON*, VOL. 5, 1824

CLEMATIS JACKMANII

Louis van Houtte, *Flore des Serres et des Jardins de l'Europe*, Vol. XVI, 1865–1867

GESNERIA BULBOSA

(PROBABLY *SINNINGIA BULBOSA*)

CALCEOLARIA ANGUSTIFLORA

(LADY'S PURSE OR SLIPPERWORT)

WILLIAM JACKSON HOOKER, *CURTIS'S BOTANICAL MAGAZINE*, VOL. 58, 1831

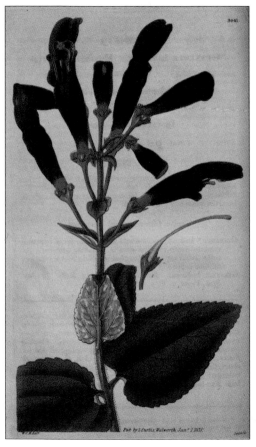

ALSTROEMERIA ACUTIFOLIA

(*BOMAREA ACUTIFOLIA*)

WILLIAM JACKSON HOOKER, *CURTIS'S BOTANICAL MAGAZINE*, VOL. 58, 1831

HUNNEMANNIA FUMARIAEFOLIA

(MEXICAN TULIP POPPY)

LONICERA HIRSUTA

(HAIRY HONEYSUCKLE)

WILLIAM JACKSON HOOKER, *CURTIS'S BOTANICAL MAGAZINE*, VOL. 58, 1831

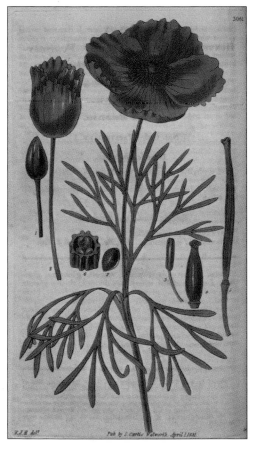

BAPTISIA PERFOLIATA

(Catbell)

WILLIAM JACKSON HOOKER, *CURTIS'S BOTANICAL MAGAZINE*, VOL. 58, 1831

ADAMIA CYANEA

ALSTROEMERIA NEILLII

WILLIAM JACKSON HOOKER, *CURTIS'S BOTANICAL MAGAZINE*, VOL. 58, 1831

ANEMONE JAPONICA

(JAPANESE ANEMONE)

WALTER HOOD FITCH, *CURTIS'S BOTANICAL MAGAZINE*, VOL. 73, 1847

CHIRONIA DECCUSSATA

(NOW *DECUSSATA*)

CHARLES McINTOSH, *THE PRACTICAL GARDENER*, VOL. 2, 1829

CHIRONIA DECCUSSATA.

London: Published by Thomas Kelly, Paternoster Row, October 1,1829.

ERYTHRONIUM DENS-CANIS

(DOG'S TOOTH VIOLET)

EDWARD DONOVAN, *THE BOTANICAL MAGAZINE*, VOL. 1, 1790

SCILLA ESCULENTA

(NOW *CAMASSIA SCILLOIDES*)

WILLIAM JACKSON HOOKER, *CURTIS'S BOTANICAL MAGAZINE*, VOL. 54, 1827

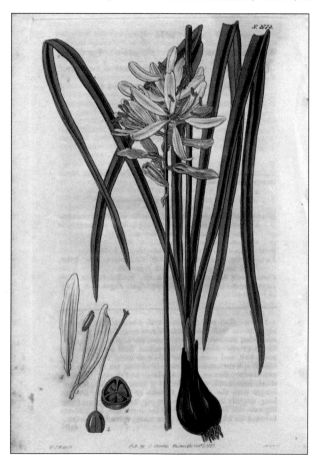

CYRTANTHUS OBLIQUUS

(SOLDIER LILY)

PIERRE JOSEPH REDOUTÉ, *CHOIX DES PLUS BELLES FLEURS*, 1827

Cyrtanthe oblique.

P. J. Redouté _ 28.

Cyrtanthus obliquus.

LAVANDULA SPICA

(LAVENDER)

GILBERT THOMAS BURNETT, *ENCYCLOPEDIA OF USEFUL AND ORNAMENTAL PLANTS*, 1852

Lavandula Spica

LILIUM LANCIFOLIUM "RUBRUM"

(RED TIGER LILY)

VICK'S MONTHLY MAGAZINE, VOL. II, 1879

LANCIFOLIUM LILY RUBRUM

AGAPANTHUS UMBELLATUS

(AFRICAN BLUE LILY)

SYDENHAM EDWARDS, *THE BOTANICAL MAGAZINE*, VOL. 14, 1800

MICHAUXIA CAMPANULOIDES

(Michaux's bellflower)

Sydenham Edwards, *The Botanical Magazine*, Vol. 7, 1794

TROPAEOLUM MAJUS

(NASTURTIUM)

JAMES SOWERBY, *THE BOTANICAL MAGAZINE*, VOL. 1, 1787

IRIS SUSIANA

THE BOTANICAL MAGAZINE, VOL. 3, 1790

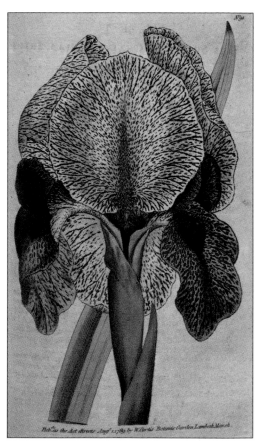

GLADIOLUS CARDINALIS

SYDENHAM EDWARDS, *THE BOTANICAL MAGAZINE*, VOL. 4, 1791

MONARDA FISTULOSA

(Wild bergamot)

Sydenham Edwards, *The Botanical Magazine*,
Vol. 5, 1792

PELARGONIUM BETULINUM

Sydenham Edwards, *The Botanical Magazine*, Vol.
5, 1792

CANNABIS SATIVA

Vienna Dioscurides, before AD 512

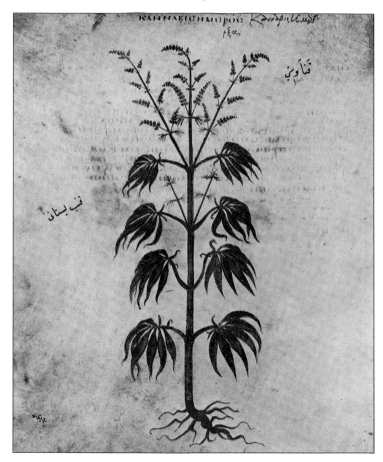

BROMELIA ANANAS

(PINEAPPLE)

PIERRE JOSEPH REDOUTÉ, *LES LILIACÉES*, VOL. 8, C. 1810

SATSUMA

WILLIAM HENRY PRESTELE, DIVISION OF POMOLOGY, U.S. DEPARTMENT OF AGRICULTURE, 1887

MESPILUS GERMANICA

(COMMON MEDLAR)

OTTO WILHELM THOMÉ, *FLORA VON DEUTSCHLAND, ÖSTERREICH UND DER SCHWEIZ*, C. 1885

CHERRY
(*PRUNUS* SPECIES)
1913

XANTHOCHYMUS DULCIS

(NOW *GARCINIA DULCIS*)

WILLIAM JACKSON HOOKER, *CURTIS'S BOTANICAL MAGAZINE*, VOL. 58, 1831

PEAR

(Pyrus gans)

From "Report of the Pomologist" in the USDA Yearbook, 1891

GANS.

FRAGARIA MONOPHYLLA
(STRAWBERRY)
THE BOTANICAL MAGAZINE, VOL. 2, 1790

PUNICA GRANATA
(POMEGRANATE)
FLORA GRAECA, VOL. 5, 1825

MISSION OLIVE

WILLIAM HENRY PRESTELE, DIVISION OF POMOLOGY, U.S. DEPARTMENT OF AGRICULTURE, 1887

CAROTTE FOURRAGÈRE

(FODDER CARROTS)

PHILIBERT NAUDIN, *NOUVELLE ICONOGRAPHIE FOURRAGÈRE*, 1871

CUCURBITA SULCATA BLANCO

(AKA *CUCURBITA MAXIMA DUCHESNE*)
FÉLIX MARTÍNEZ, *FLORA DE FILIPINAS*, VOL. III, 1879

CUCURBITA SULCATA —BLANCO.
CUCURBITA MAXIMA.—DUCH.— DC.
VAR. VIRIDIS.— DC.

RHODODENDRON FULGENS

(Brilliant rhododendron)

Walter Hood Fitch, *Curtis's Botanical Magazine*, Vol. 88, 1862

RHODODENDRON JAVANICUM

(JAVANESE RHODODENDRON)

WALTER HOOD FITCH, *CURTIS'S BOTANICAL MAGAZINE*, VOL. 73, 1847

PADUS AVIUM MILLER

(Bird cherry)

Otto Wilhelm Thomé, *Flora von Deutschland, Österreich und der Schweiz*, c. 1885

COTONEASTER INTERRIMA MEDICUS

(WILD COTONEASTER)

Otto Wilhelm Thomé, *Flora von Deutschland, Österreich und der Schweiz*, c. 1885

NIRIUM ODORUM

(NERIUM OLEANDER)
HORTUS MALABARICUS, PART 9, 1689

VIBURNUM RUGOSUM

(AKA *VIBURNUM TINUS*)

CURTIS'S BOTANICAL MAGAZINE, VOL. 46, 1819

CAMELLIA MME P DE PANNEMAEKER CORDATUM

PIETER DE PANNEMAEKER,
L'ILLUSTRATION HORTICOLE, 1880S

CAMELLIA MADAME P DE PANNEMAEKER

CAMELLIA THEA

(CAMELLIA SINENSIS (L.) KUNTZE)
KÖHLER'S MEDIZINAL-PFLANZEN, 1890

ANNONA SQUAMOSA

(Sugar apple)

Rev. Lansdown Guilding, *Curtis's Botanical Magazine*, Vol. 58, 1831

SORBUS AUCUPARIA

(Rowan or Mountain ash)

Otto Wilhelm Thomé, *Flora von Deutschland, Österreich und der Schweiz*, c. 1885

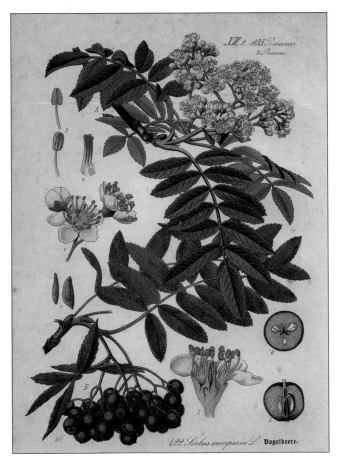

CRATAEGUS OXYACANTHA

(HAWTHORN)

OTTO WILHELM THOMÉ, *FLORA VON DEUTSCHLAND, ÖSTERREICH UND DER SCHWEIZ*, C. 1885

PRUNUS SPINOZA

(Blackthorn or sloe)

Otto Wilhelm Thomé, *Flora von Deutschland, Österreich und der Schweiz*, c. 1885

ACHRAS SAPOTA

(Sapota tree)

Rev. Lansdown Guilding, *Curtis's Botanical Magazine*, Vol. 58, 1831

POLYPODIUM DRYOPTERIS

(AKA *GYMNOCARPIUM DRYOPTERIS*)

WALTER HOOD FITCH, *A POPULAR HISTORY OF BRITISH FERNS AND ALLIED PLANTS*, 1851

Plate II.

WALTER HOOD FITCH, *A POPULAR HISTORY OF BRITISH FERNS AND ALLIED PLANTS*, 1851

Plate III.

ARUM CAMPANULATUM

(AKA *AMORPHOPHALLUS PAEONIIFOLIUS*)
CURTIS'S BOTANICAL MAGAZINE, VOL. 55, 1828

COLUMNEA HIRSUTA

CURTIS'S BOTANICAL MAGAZINE, VOL. 58, 1831

NEPENTHES RAFFLESIANA

(RAFFLES' PITCHER-PLANT)

WALTER HOOD FITCH, *CURTIS'S BOTANICAL MAGAZINE*, VOL. 73, 1847

HEDYCHIUM FLAVUM

(GINGER LILY)

WALTER HOOD FITCH, *CURTIS'S BOTANICAL MAGAZINE*, VOL. 58, 1831

CODIAEUM PICTUM

(AKA *CROTON VARIEGATUM*)

WILLIAM JACKSON HOOKER, *CURTIS'S BOTANICAL MAGAZINE*, VOL. 58, 1831

BEGONIA FUCHSIOIDES

WALTER HOOD FITCH, *CURTIS'S BOTANICAL MAGAZINE*, VOL. 73, 1847

THIBAUDIA PULCHERRIMA

(AKA *AGAPETES VARIEGATA*)

CURTIS'S BOTANICAL MAGAZINE, VOL. 73, 1847

AESCHYNANTHUS SPECIOSUS

(Basket plant)

Walter Hood Fitch, *Curtis's Botanical Magazine*,
Vol. 73, 1847

MAXILLARIA TETRAGONA

(*Orchidaceae aka Bifrenaria tetragona*)

Curtis's Botanical Magazine, Vol. 59, 1832

PUYA ALTENSTEINII, VAR. GIGANTEA

Curtis's Botanical Magazine, Vol. 73, 1847

MEDINILLA SPECIOSA

(Showy Asian grapes)

Walter Hood Fitch, *Curtis's Botanical Magazine*, Vol. 73, 1847

IXORA GRIFFITHII

(AKA *IXORA CONGESTA ROXB.*)

WALTER HOOD FITCH, *CURTIS'S BOTANICAL MAGAZINE*, VOL. 73, 1847

EUCALYPTUS MACROCARPA

Walter Hood Fitch, *Curtis's Botanical Magazine*, Vol. 73, 1847

STRELITZIA REGINAE

THE BOTANICAL MAGAZINE, VOL. 4, 1790

Pub. as the Act directs, May 1.1790. by W. Curtis, S.' Georges Crescent.

GRAMMANGIS ELLISII

(*ORCHIDACEAE*)

WALTER HOOD FITCH, *CURTIS'S BOTANICAL MAGAZINE*, VOL. 86, 1860

BRASSIA LANCEANA

(*ORCHIDACEAE*)

WALTER HOOD FITCH, *CURTIS'S BOTANICAL MAGAZINE*, VOL. 64, 1837

RENANTHERA COCCINEA

(*ORCHIDACEAE*)

WILLIAM JACKSON HOOKER, *CURTIS'S BOTANICAL MAGAZINE*, VOL. 57, 1830

ONCIDIUM ALTISSIMUM

(*ORCHIDACEAE*)

WILLIAM JACKSON HOOKER, *CURTIS'S BOTANICAL MAGAZINE*, VOL. 57, 1830

ONCIDIUM PAPILIO

(NOW *PSYCHOPSIS PAPILIO*)
WILLIAM JACKSON HOOKER, *CURTIS'S BOTANICAL MAGAZINE*, VOL. 55, 1828

MICROSTYLIS DISCOLOR

(*ORCHIDACEAE* AKA MALAXIS DISCOLOR)
WALTER HOOD FITCH, *CURTIS'S BOTANICAL MAGAZINE*, VOL. 89, 1863

PERISTERIA ELATA

(*ORCHIDACEAE*)

Mrs. Arnold Harrison, *Curtis's Botanical Magazine*, Vol. 58, 1831

MELOCACTUS COMMUNIS

William Jackson Hooker, *Curtis's Botanical Magazine*, Vol. 58, 1831

ECHINOCACTUS HEXAEDROPHORUS

WALTER HOOD FITCH, *CURTIS'S BOTANICAL MAGAZINE*, VOL. 73, 1847

BANKSIA INTEGRIFOLIA

(*COAST BANKSIA*)

WILLIAM JACKSON HOOKER, *CURTIS'S BOTANICAL MAGAZINE*, VOL. 54, 1827

DRYANDRA ARMATA

(AKA *BANKSIA ARMATA*)

WILLIAM JACKSON HOOKER, *CURTIS'S BOTANICAL MAGAZINE*, VOL. 60, 1833

VICTORIA AMAZONICA

(*NYMPHAEACEAE*)

WALTER HOOD FITCH, *CURTIS'S BOTANICAL MAGAZINE*, VOL. 73, 1847

VICTORIA AMAZONICA

(*NYMPHAEACEAE*)

WALTER HOOD FITCH, *CURTIS'S BOTANICAL MAGAZINE*, VOL. 73, 1847

INDEX OF PLANT NAMES